DOMESTICITY ISN'T PRETTY

A *Leonard&Larry* COLLECTION BY

Palliard Press

Palliard Press
Minneapolis 1993

FIRST EDITION

Published by Palliard Press
c/o DreamHaven Books
1309 Fourth Street S.E.
Minneapolis, Minnesota
55414-2029

Book Design by Robert T. Garcia and Tim Barela

ISBN 1-884568-00-9

PRINTED IN THE UNITED STATES OF AMERICA

Dedicated with great
affection to the memory of

Jerry Mills

*A wonderful cartoonist
and a good friend who's
enthusiasm, encouragement
and diligent advocation
helped put my cartoons
on the map, a man
who friends of Leonard and
Larry's, everywhere, owe
a debt of gratitude*

CONTENTS

FORWARD

by John Preston

I've read Tim Barela's comic strips for years. They've been a consistent attraction whenever I've picked up, at first, *The Advocate* and, later, *Frontiers*. I've always considered them some of the best gay literature we have. This man understands that there are stories to tell in our lives, and he doesn't try to be cutesy literary by setting those stories on prep school campuses or on chic Long Island resorts. I've never really understood why, but somehow it seems that many people are convinced that a narrative set in St. Paul's or on the shores of Fire Island somehow becomes more *important*. I think this is a very strange and self-defeating deception. The best stories are set in the place where they happen. That's when their authenticity can shine through. And Barela has authenticity in spades. His on the mark material shows us what we look like, in all our wonderfully flawed humanity.

Barela understands a basic point that many others would be well-advised to remember: the best way to deal with stereotypes is to encounter them, look at them deeply, examine just what's behind them. While it's easy to dismiss what appears on first examination to be a cliche and to pass judgement on its single dimension, it becomes more difficult to dismiss that image when it's fleshed out. That's one of the functions of art, to give what might seem commonplace a new measure.

Take a perhaps overtly arty gay photographer who at least occasionally has work in *Vanity Fair,* add as his lover an outcast from Orange County who has found his place in the world as the owner of a leather shop on Melrose Avenue, give them a house in West Hollywood, and you have the beginning of a major gay stereotype. They could be exactly the kind of fags that people like to sneer at—one dimensional would be the kindest way to describe them.

Tim Barela has taken just that material and he's performed genius. His drawings and story lines take us behind the facades and into the minds and lives of these men, Larry and Leonard. With a guide as competent as Barela, we no longer just see a facade, we start to see human beings.

It's not a great surprise that Barela's key to creating depth in these characters is to put them in the context of their families. Larry has two children from a previous heterosexual marriage. Leonard has a mother right out of your nightmares and sibling rivalry that could launch ships.

The men's homosexuality—and their specific proclivities—aren't the driving force in Barela's work. In fact, usually they're only background for the stories he has to tell. Being gay certainly does add something to Larry and Leonard's life, it brings them together as a couple, it adds to their sense of cynicism and rage against a homophobic society, it gives a passion to their being. Yet the real dramas they live out are the dramas that everyone lives out whether in leather drag or suburban obscurity.

There is aging. Any man in his forties who reads this work and listens to Larry's angst over his age is going to know just what's going on. There it is, the middle-life crisis that we all go through. There are children. Any parent can see his or herself in Larry's encounters with his kids. And there are our own parents. Even when Leonard puts Larry on guard duty to protect him from his mother, she finds a way into the house.

Probably the most interesting twist Barela has spun in all this is to have David, Larry's younger son, come out. That Larry is something of a sexual outlaw with his leather shop doesn't mean a thing when he's confronted with his boy's homosexuality. There's still a trauma. And, as Barela so subtly shows us, it's really not that different than the trauma of the older son becoming a father. These are the plots of daily life in middle-class America that have about them the stuff of literature, not just sitcom plots, when they're handled by a storyteller with Barela's skill.

INTRODUCTION

by Andy Mangels

**A HOLLYWOOD
PITCH MEETING**

"Okay, so what's next? *Leonard & Larry?* Is this one yours, Cosgrove?"

"Yes, sir. It's a totally new, revolutionary idea for a sit-com that..."

"Gimme the high concept."

"*My Two Dads* meets *The Donna Reed Show.*"

"Hmmmmm. Retro but modern. Go on."

"Okay, so it's got these two men living in West Hollywood, dealing with two teen-age sons, an ex-wife, a trendy leather store and..."

"Wait. Two teenage sons? Sounds more like *My Three Sons.* Can we add a couple of girls, maybe twins... or triplets! Yeah."

"What's the other one do?"

"He's a photographer."

"Great, lots of star cameos. Maybe he shoots for the *Enquirer* or something. Can we get Charo?"

"Gary Coleman's dying for a guest role."

"Cool, Wilton. Can we get him on as one of these kids? Get that interracial family thing going? Maybe have him do some hip-hop?"

"Ummm, the creator really wants us to stick to his vision here. I think it's really fresh. It's been appearing as a comic strip for years, and it's very popular."

This is Tim Barela's first published comic strip. The unnamed series ran in *Cycle News.* Mitch Hays (with dark hair) and the unnamed Yamaha parts person (based physically on a friend of Tim's) were to become series regulars.

"Errrrrr, comic strips are risky. *The Flash* didn't do so hot. Where's it been appearing? I haven't seen it."

"Well, *The Advocate, Frontiers, Gay Comics*..."

"Whoah. Hold on a second. Those are all gay magazines. Do you mean to tell me these two men are..."

"Yes, sir."

"And the leather store is..."

"Well, yes, I guess so."

"Next pitch."

"Leonard & Larry" creator, Tim Barela, has always seen his strip as a modern-day sit-com, replacing the requisite married heterosexuals with a pair of "married" homosexuals. Appearing in a gay comics scene wherein the vast majority of cartoonists deal with political and sexual issues—and almost no one deals with couples in the context of domestic and family situations—"Leonard & Larry" is a remarkable achievement.

Tim Barela's background is far removed from the rather "mainstream" gay lives of Leonard Goldman and Larry Evans. To meet him is to encounter a burly bear of a man with a long black ponytail and beard (both starting to grey), and who is normally attired in black t-shirts and biker regalia. Contrary to the urban, West Hollywood environs that his characters frequent, Tim lives in a semi-rural corner of California, hours from downtown Los Angeles. And unlike his 'toon creations, he has neither children or grandchildren, nor

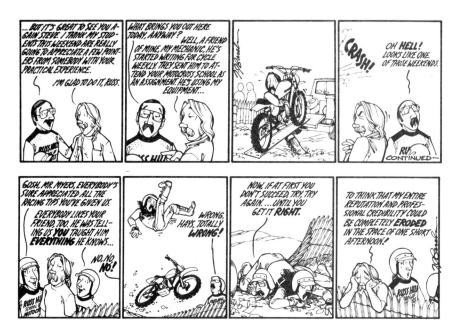

Note that Steve Meyers (light-haired) and Mitch Hays bear a resemblance to Leonard and Larry, several years before Tim conceived of or drew his most famous characters!

Late in the series, Tim based this sequence on a true-life six-month wait for parts following his own motorcycle accident.

has he been married or involved in an extended relationship, gay, straight or otherwise!

Born in Los Angeles in 1954, of Spanish, German and Cherokee extraction, Tim never read comics as a child. Instead, he grew up fascinated by newspaper "funny pages" and animated cartoons on television, especially *The Flintstones, The Jetsons, Huckleberry Hound* and other Hanna-Barbera offerings. Having started drawing at age three, Tim often copied cartoon characters from these media sources.

The benign, family-oriented television situations comedies of the early 1960s were also a staple of his early entertainment diet. Ultimately, Tim's sense of storytelling was challenged by *All In The Family,* a sitcom which altered his opinion of what good comedy writing could do and say. When Garry Trudeau's *Doonesbury* began in newspapers, Tim realized that comics could also address important issues. It was about this time that he had been submitting single panel gag cartoons to magazines as diverse as the *Saturday Evening Post* and *Playboy,* receiving only rejection slips.

By the mid-1970s, Tim began taking his cartooning seriously, submitting his work, still without success, to various newspaper syndicates. In 1976, his talent and tenacity won him a job, and he began contributing regularly to the sports weekly, *Cycle News.* They paid him

Hard Tail and Worm are the best of friends in *Choppers'* "Hard Tale." though dealing with a mainly heterosexual audience, and despite not having come to terms with his own homosexuality, Tim's later strip dealt explicitly with gay themes in a remarkably supportive way.

the princely sum of ten dollars per installment of his unnamed comic strip.

His work began to attract the notice of other motorcycle publications; soon, other offers came in. His strips included "Just Puttin'" in *Biker* (1977-78), "Short Strokes" in *Cycle World* (July 1977-February 1979), "Hard Tale" in *Choppers* (Sept. 1978-79) and untitled strips in *FTW News* (1979). This last newspaper later became *Biker Lifestyle*, for which Tim drew various strips, including "The Adventures of Rickie Racer," the *CHiPs*-like "The Adventures of Erick Enchilada," and the bizarre biker-as-a-cooking-expert strip, "The Puttin' Gourmet... America's Favorite Low-Life Epicurean."

Though cycle enthusiasts often consider themselves to be open-minded, they are not normally supportive of "alternative lifestyles." Nonetheless, Tim, who had been a fundamentalist Christian since high school, began to come to grips with his suppressed homosexuality at this time. In May 1979, he drew a "Hard Tale" strip in which Hard Tail and Worm, the biker heroes of the series, accidentally ended up in a gay bar, and came down with a case of heterosexual panic. This was Barela's first foray into dealing with gay issues.

When Ronald Reagan was elected, the realization of how politically oriented fundamentalist churches were affected him profoundly. Turned off by what he saw as an agenda of preaching poli-

Tim's best gag for *Cycle World* from November 1978.

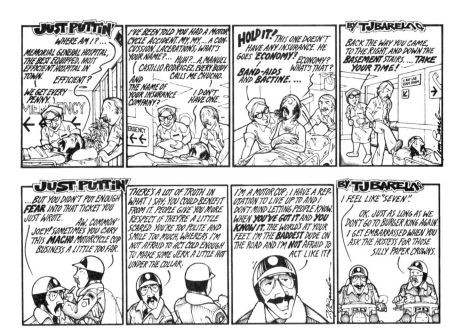

The "Just Puttin'" strip ran in *Biker*, and it featured a pair of motorcycle cops named Doug and Joey, and two bikers named Stud Marrone and Chucho Rodrigez. Doug and Stud were based on church friends of Tim's.

tics from the pulpit, he left the church. Ultimately, in 1980 Tim started attending the gay-friendly Metropolitan Community Church in Long Beach.

That year, he made another attempt at a syndicated newspaper strip with "Ozone," a series about the friendship between suburban Santa Monica neighbors, including a straight man named Rodger, and a gay man named Leonard Goldman. Leonard eventually got a "roommate" named Larry Evans. The strip didn't fly, and was later relocated to inner-city Los Angeles, where Leonard, Larry, Rodger and his wife Susan, reappeared. Again the strip didn't go anywhere, but Barela couldn't abandon the characters. He decided to make Leonard and Larry the focus of a new series.

Prompted by friends and the "sweater-wearing gay Republicans" in his Los Feliz Bible Study group, Tim submitted samples of the reworked strip to *The Advocate* (a national bi-weekly gay newsmagazine), and was flatly turned down with a tersely-worded, two-line rejection letter. The samples eventually found their way into the hands of Robert Triptow, then the editor of *Gay Comix*. Triptow liked what he saw and asked Tim to produce longer stories.

"Leonard & Larry" made its first published appearance in *Gay Comix* #5 in 1984. The refreshing strip became a popular staple of the underground comic series, appear-

Leonard and Larry made their very first appearances as Rodger and Susan's gay next door neighbors in "Ozone," one of Tim's many unsuccessful quests for a nationally syndicated newspaper feature in the early 1980s. Fortunately, Leonard and Larry survived the demise of "Ozone" and its dated humor concerning such things as the pop psychology book, *I'm OK, You're OK*.

ing in issues #6-7 and #10-13. Tim later contributed a two-page "Leonard & Larry" sequence for an AIDS benefit book called *Strip AIDS USA* which was co-edited by Triptow.

In 1987, Tim finally did land a syndication contract. The Louisiana-based Americomics, Inc. was a new syndicator in the market, targeting weekly newspapers throughout the country. They signed him up for "Komrades," which featured a Russian defector, Yuri Sakov, who had been pulled from the waters of Galveston Bay by a Texas fisherman named Dale Cox. The strip dealt more with culture clash than politics, but never saw print. After twelve installments were completed, Americomics, Inc. disbanded due to loss of financial backing.

Not long afterward, Tim approached the editors of *Bear* magazine (an erotic gay bi-monthly) about creating a new strip for them. Impressed by his work in *Gay Comix*, they agreed. Barela called the series "Grizzly & Ted," but only one story ran (in issue #5, 1988, reprinted in *Gay Comix* #14). Tim would have continued the series, but a bigger offer was in the wings.

Spurred on by fellow cartoonist, Jerry Mills, the new editorial staff of *The Advocate* approached Tim about "Leonard & Larry." A more comics-friendly editor liked what he saw, and the strip joined Alison Bechdel's "Servants to the Cause" and

"Komrades" was to appear in weekly papers across the country addressing issues of "east-meets-west" in a very literal context. Unfortunately, the syndicate folded before the strip could start. This is the first publication on any of the twelve completed installments.

Gerald Donelan's "It's A Gay Life," as regular features. Starting with the December 5, 1988/ #513 issue, "Leonard & Larry" ran in a rotating once-a-month spot.

A new editor and a new decade brought different directions and content changes to The *Advocate*. Unfortunately, the changes meant dropping Tim and Alison's strips with the September 25, 1990/#60 issue. Fans didn't have long to mourn though; the loyalty Tim found in *Advocate* readers inspired *Frontiers* magazine (an *Advocate* competitor) to adopt "Leonard & Larry." It first appeared— cover-blurbed no less!—in the October 26, 1990 issue. It still appears in that bi-weekly, to this day.

Although uncomfortable in the comic book world, Tim appeared for the first time at the San Diego Comic Con in 1989, on a discussion panel promoting *Strip AIDS USA*. Two years later, he again attended the convention to take part in the panel called "Gays In Comics." Shortly after the release of *Gay Comix* #1 (Spring 1992), which collected much of *The Advocate* and some *Frontiers* material, Barela appeared at the convention again and did a book signing. By 1993's San Diego Comic Con, Tim had contracted to publish the book you now hold in your hands. Sponsored by Palliard Press, Tim had become much better known in the comic industry. Ashcan editions (pre-publication smaller

"The Puttin' Gourmet" ran in various issues of *Biker Lifestyle*. The Harley-riding cook had a wicked sense of humor and a foul mouth, showcasing Tim's more (rarely seen) twisted cartooning style. The strip was usually among the tamest features of the magazine.

copies) were available for fans to see, and audience members at the "Gays In Comics" panel gave him an extended ovation.

Currently, Tim is working hard on producing "Leonard & Larry" every two weeks for *Frontiers* and does commercial design work on the side. He's readying a new strip about a mixed gay and lesbian household for future issues of *Gay Comics*. He's also looking forward to the Spring 1994 premiere of "Leonard & Larry" on stage in San Francisco. The Theatre Rhinoceros production of the comic strip, *Leonard & Larry, A Domestic Comedy*, will be one of four segments in an evening entitled "Out Of The Inkwell." Kelly Kittell adapted the pregnancy and birth sequence which appears in this very book.

And, the "Leonard & Larry" sitcom discussed at the beginning of the introduction? Well, given the excellence of the source material, you can bet that we'll be seeing it eventually.

Andy Mangels is the editor of Gay Comics *and is a comic book writer and journalist. He's worked on* Elfquest: Blood of Ten Chiefs, Nightmares on Elm Street *and* Hero Illustrated, *among many others.*

In *FTW News'* "The Adventures of Erick Enchilada," Tim poked fun at the adventures of a Highway Patrol officer who seemed more than a little similar to a certain late-70s TV cop/sex symbol. Tim managed to slip in some early political references, as well as a few familiar looking types that we'd see more of in "Leonard & Larry."

Tim continues to put his friends in his cartoons, as can be seen in this very book. Look for comedian/registered nurse "Lurch" as Nurse Mike in the birth sequence, and introduction author Andy Mangels as Father Andrew towards the end of the book.

DOMESTICITY ISN'T PRETTY

Gay Comix 1984-1987

...WE'LL START OFF WITH MY STUFFED CRAB **PUFFS** AND THE MUSHROOM **QUICHE**, FOLLOWED BY **CHICKEN DIVAN** AND SPINACH **CRÊPES**. WE'LL TOP THE WHOLE THING OFF WITH **'75 CHÂTEAU-NEUF-du PAPE**.

THAT'S THE **SWISHIEST** SOUNDING MENU YOU'VE EVER COME UP WITH! WHAT AN IMPRESSION WE'LL MAKE; THAT NICE, **STRAIGHT** COUPLE THAT MOVED IN NEXT DOOR IS GOING TO LEAVE THIS DINNER PARTY THINKING WE'RE A COUPLE OF **RAVING QUEENS!**

BUT, SWEETHEART, WE **ARE.**

WE HAVE TO **DO** SOMETHING **APPROPRIATE** FOR **DESSERT.**

HOW ABOUT A NICE **FRUIT FLAMBÉ?**

PERFECT!

RECIPES

20

RICHARD, DAVID, JUST TEN MORE MINUTES. I HAVE TO HAVE YOU BACK AT YOUR MOTHER'S BY FIVE O'CLOCK.

OH YEAH? WELL MY DAD OWNS HIS OWN STORE. HE SELLS LEATHER JACKETS N' BOOTS, N' LOTS OF OTHER LEATHER STUFF WE'RE **NOT** SUPPOSED TA' TALK ABOUT.

YEAH, AND HE'S **QUEER,** TOO.

TIM BARELA — ©1983

DAD'S NOT **QUEER,** DAVID, HE'S **GAY.**

WELL, YEAH, THAT **TOO.**

GOSH, MY DAD'S **JUST A MAILMAN.**

GUESS WE'RE JUST **LUCKY.**

YEAH!

21

WAIT,...DON'T GO INSIDE YET. SOMETHING'S **WRONG!** ...MY **MOTHER'S** HERE.

WHAT?

I CAN TELL...

...REMEMBER, SHE CONNED THAT EXTRA KEY SO SHE COULD GET IN IF WE WERE GONE—I CAN **SMELL** THE **CARE PACKAGE** OF **CHICKEN SOUP** AND **LOX.**

IF SHE IS HERE, WHY WOULD SHE BE SITTING IN THE **DARK?**

BECAUSE A **GOOD MOTHER** DOESN'T COME INTO HER SON'S HOUSE AND **WASTE** ALL OF HIS HARD EARNED **ELECTRICITY.**

...LENNY, I MET SUCH A NICE **GIRL** THE OTHER DAY. **SYLVIA BLOOM,** TWENTY NINE AND **SINGLE.** ...**YOU'D** LIKE HER.

MAYBE, IF WE **IGNORE IT** AND GO BACK TO THE BAR FOR A WHILE, IT'LL **GO AWAY.**

I SHOULD LIVE SO LONG.

TIM BARELA ©1983

23

YOU MEAN LIKE THE WAY YOU HANDLED YOUR MOTHER LAST WEEK? GREAT JOB, LEONARD! BECAUSE OF YOUR EXPERTISE, A CERTAIN MONOGAMOUS, GAY COUPLE IS GOING ON A BLIND, DOUBLE DATE TONIGHT... WITH TWO WOMEN!

LARRY, WHAT'S THE BIG DEAL? WE'LL GO TO DINNER AND THE SHOW; HAVE A NICE TIME. WE'LL APPEASE MY MOTHER'S WRATH AND THAT WILL BE THAT.

LEONARD, DON'T YOU SEE? IF YOU LET YOUR MOTHER GET AWAY WITH THIS ONCE, THE SECOND TIME'LL BE A BREEZE! AND SHE'S NOT PLAYING GAMES EITHER. BELIEVE ME, THESE WOMEN MOTHERS TRY TO FIX THEIR SONS UP WITH HAVE ONLY ONE THING ON THEIR MINDS—MARRIAGE! SOME INNOCENT BLIND DATE SOME DAY YOU'RE GOING TO FIND YOURSELF ON THE FREEWAY HALF WAY TO LAS VEGAS WHILE I SIT AT HOME KEEPING DINNER WARM IN THE OVEN!!

KNOCK KNOCK KNOCK

YOU DON'T KNOW WHAT YOU'RE TALKING ABOUT.

OH YEAH? HOW DO YOU THINK I ENDED UP MARRIED FOR EIGHT YEARS WITH TWO KIDS?! MY MOTHER WAS QUITE A YENTA FOR A METHODIST!

2

LOOK, EVERYONE, SUCH A SURPRISE! IT'S MY SINGLE SON LEONARD AND HIS FRIEND, LAWRENCE.

LAWRENCE?

LEONARD, YOU'RE SO THIN! LISTEN, I HAVE A NICE PIECE OF BRISKET IN THE FRIDGE, I'LL MAKE YOU A SANDWICH BEFORE DINNER.

MOTHER!

MOTHER!

OH NO, NOT AGAIN!

MOTHER, YOU TOLD US WE WERE GOING WITH MRS. GOLDMAN TO A TUPPERWARE PARTY!

WHY WOULD YOU WANT TO GO AND LOOK AT PLASTIC DISHES WHEN YOU CAN GO OUT WITH TWO HANDSOME YOUNG MEN?

YOU MEAN LIKE THE LAST TWO LOSERS YOU FIXED US UP WITH? THEY WERE A COUPLE OF MACHO, CHAUVINIST JERKS! THEY TOOK US TO A TACKY VIDEO SINGLES BAR WITH CHROME FURNITURE AND CARPETED WALLS AT THE MARINA. THEIR ENTIRE PERSONALITIES CONSISTED OF HANDS AND HORMONES!

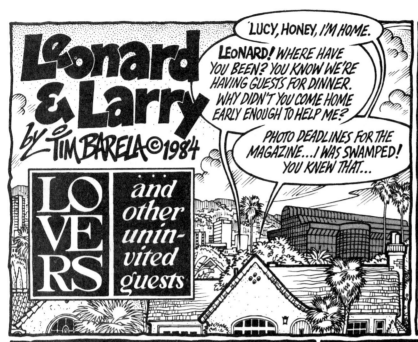

Leonard & Larry
by Tim Barela ©1984

LOVERS *...and other uninvited guests*

"LUCY, HONEY, I'M HOME."

LEONARD! WHERE HAVE YOU BEEN? YOU KNOW WE'RE HAVING GUESTS FOR DINNER. WHY DIDN'T YOU COME HOME EARLY ENOUGH TO HELP ME?

PHOTO DEADLINES FOR THE MAGAZINE...I WAS SWAMPED! YOU KNEW THAT...

...BESIDES, I THOUGHT WE WERE GOING OUT TO EAT.

FOR CHRISSAKES, LEONARD! OF ALL DAYS, WHY DID YOU WEAR THAT FAGGOTTY LAVENDER AND TURQUOISE ABORTION TODAY? PLEASE GO PUT SOMETHING NICE AND CONSERVATIVE ON.

LET HE WHO IS WITHOUT SIN CAST THE FIRST SLICE OF QUICHE.

DON'T START IN ON ME, LEONARD! I HAD TO START DINNER AS SOON AS I GOT HOME FROM WORK; I HAVEN'T HAD TIME TO CHANGE... EVER TRIED SLAVING OVER A HOT STOVE IN BLACK LEATHER BEFORE?

REALLY, LARRY, I DON'T THINK EITHER DENNIS OR LEON WILL CARE HOW WE'RE DRESSED.

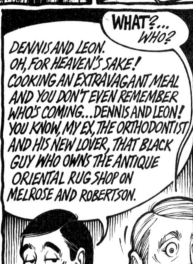

WHAT?... WHO?

DENNIS AND LEON. OH, FOR HEAVEN'S SAKE! COOKING AN EXTRAVAGANT MEAL AND YOU DON'T EVEN REMEMBER WHO'S COMING...DENNIS AND LEON! YOU KNOW, MY EX, THE ORTHODONTIST, AND HIS NEW LOVER, THAT BLACK GUY WHO OWNS THE ANTIQUE ORIENTAL RUG SHOP ON MELROSE AND ROBERTSON.

THE "TOOTH FAIRY" AND THE "AFRICAN QUEEN"?!

LEONARD, MY EX-WIFE AND HER NEW FIANCÉE ARE COMING TO DINNER TONIGHT. SHARON SAYS THAT THIS GUY IS A MEMBER OF SOME MOLDY OLD ANAHEIM FAMILY THAT'S PRACTICALLY THE ORANGE COUNTY DISTRIBUTER FOR THE MORAL MAJORITY!

WHY ON EARTH DID YOU INVITE THEM TO DINNER TONIGHT? I TOLD YOU WEEKS AGO THAT DENNIS AND LEON...

YOU SAID THAT THEY WERE COMING ON THE SIXTEENTH.

NOT THE SIXTEENTH, THE SIXTH...TODAY!

OH MY GOD! ...WHAT HAVE I DONE?!

I'D SAY YOU'VE DONE A LOVELY JOB WITH DINNER; TASTEFULLY BUTCH... ROAST BEEF, BAKED POTATOES, SPINACH. SHOULD COMPLEMENT THE CRAB MEAT SOUFFLÉ AND WHITE WINE DENNIS AND LEON ARE BRINGING FOR APPETIZERS JUST WONDERFULLY...I'LL SET A COUPLE OF EXTRA PLACES AT THE TABLE.

DON'T BE RIDICULOUS, LEONARD! WE CAN'T...

DING DONG

HOLY SHIT, THEY'RE EARLY! I HAVE TO CHANGE!

OH NO! I'M NOT GOING TO SIT HERE AND ENTERTAIN YOUR EX-WIFE AND SOME REFUGEE FROM BEHIND THE ORANGE CURTAIN WHILE YOU TAKE A HALF HOUR TRYING TO DECIDE WHAT TO WEAR.

33

...SWEET CAKES! I DIDN'T RECOGNIZE YOU; LONG TIME, NO SEE! WHAT ARE YOU DOING IN THIS NECK OF THE WOODS IN THE MIDDLE OF THE WEEK? I THOUGHT YOU ONLY MADE IT UP HERE TO CRUISE SANTA MONICA BOULEVARD ON FRIDAY NIGHTS!

"SWEET CAKES"?

I SEE YOU'VE ACQUIRED A TASTE FOR BEEFY LEATHER BEARS THIS WEEK, YOU LITTLE TROLLOP! ...OH YEAH, GORDY AND I GO WAY BACK. I MET HIM ONE NIGHT WHILE I WAS WAITING FOR A BUS ON HIGHLAND AND SANTA MONICA. THIS NUMBER ACTUALLY THOUGHT I WAS A HUSTLER BECAUSE I WAS WEARING GREEN ATHLETIC SHORTS!...

...A NOVICE FOR DAYS! BUT THEN, THAT WAS MONTHS AGO; THE GIRL LEARNS FAST. LET ME TELL YA, HON, I MAY HAVE BEEN HER FIRST, BUT I DEFINITELY WASN'T THE LAST.

SO, WHICH ONE OF YOU OTHER GUYS IS D. SEAGEL?

IN THERE. GLASSES, MUSTACHE, BALD SPOT; SHOULD BE SCRAPING UNDER-COOKED CRAB MEAT SOUFFLÉ OFF OF A SHORT, BLACK MAN.

OOO, KINKY!

"SWEET CAKES."

EXCUSE ME, GENTLEMEN...SHARON, SWEET HEART, WHENEVER YOU'RE READY. I'LL BE WAITING OUT IN THE CAR...UNDER THE DASHBOARD, SOMEWHERE.

WELL, SHARON, SORRY YOU CAN'T STAY. THANKS FOR COMING THOUGH. IT WAS...ENTERTAINING.

LARRY?

YA SURE KNOW HOW TA PICK US, DON'T YA?

THE CHILD SUPPORT PAYMENT, ON TIME NEXT MONTH OR ELSE!

TIM BARELA ©1984

34

BUT... BUT... WHAT ABOUT LEONARD?

WHO?

LEONARD... MY LOVER.

OH, HIM. ...WELL, IF HE WANTS HE CAN JOIN US IN A THREE WAY SOMETIME, BUT NOT TONIGHT...

BUT LEONARD AND I ARE MONOGAMOUS.

OH, FOR HEAVEN'S SAKE!...GIVE ME A BREAK, GIRL; THIS IS THE 1980's! I KNOW THAT MONOGAMY IS BACK IN STYLE THESE DAYS, BUT REALLY!...ARE YOU TRYING TO TELL ME THAT LEONARD SPENDS ALL DAY WORKING WITH THOSE HOT MODELS IN HIS PHOTOGRAPHY STUDIO AND YOU SPEND ALL DAY OUTFITTING THESE HUNKS HERE IN YOUR LEATHER SHOP, AND NEITHER OF YOU HAS EVER BEEN, AT LEAST, TEMPTED TO FOOL AROUND?

...I MEAN, COME ON. THINGS BETWEEN YOU 'N' LEONARD CAN'T BE SO GREAT THAT MAKING IT WITH ME WOULDN'T BE...A NICE CHANGE OF PACE? HMMM?... LIFE IS SO SHORT...

LATER...

LEONARD?

I'M IN THE DINING ROOM, GOING THRU THE MAIL.

LEONARD, WE HAVE TO TALK...

I AGREE; THERE'S A LITTLE PROMOTIONAL PACKAGE HERE ADDRESSED TO "THE LADY OF THE HOUSE." ...WOULD YOU RATHER OPEN IT, OR SHOULD I?

LEONARD!

OH, FOR HEAVEN'S SAKE, IT'S A JOKE, HA-HA....LISTEN, BEFORE YOU SAY ANYTHING, I JUST WANT TO SAY I'M SORRY FOR BEING SUCH AN ASSHOLE ALL WEEK. IT'S BEEN A BITCH OF A MONTH FOR BOTH OF US, AND I THINK I KNOW WHAT WE SHOULD DO ABOUT IT...

WHAT?

...WELL, WE REALLY HAVEN'T SPENT ANY QUALITY TIME TOGETHER FOR WEEKS. ...ALL WORK AND NO PLAY... I MADE RESERVATIONS FOR PALM SPRINGS. A ROMANTIC WEEKEND IN THE DESERT, JUST YOU AND ME.

WELL,....UH, I DON'T KNOW...I MEAN, IF YOU WANT TO GO...THAT IS, HAVE YOU EVER CONSIDERED THAT, MAYBE, WHAT PEOPLE IN A RELATIONSHIP NEED, NOW AND THEN, ISN'T MORE TIME TOGETHER, BUT, WELL, YOU KNOW... TIME APART...

...I HAVEN'T LOST THE TOUCH, YOU KNOW. I STILL REMEMBER HOW TO *CRUISE* DARK, SMOKY *BARS.*

OH YEAH?

YEAH! IN FACT, I THINK I'LL GO OUT *TONIGHT;* THE *GAUNTLET* IS STILL WALL-TO-WALL *FLESH* ON FRIDAY NIGHT, ISN'T IT?

MAYBE.

I CAN WEAR *YOUR* FAVORITE TIGHT, FADED 501's WITH MY "CHEAP'N' EASY" T-SHIRT AND THE BLACK WORK BOOTS *YOU* GAVE ME FOR MY BIRTHDAY.

THAT SHOULD MAKE FOR GOOD *FISHING.*

GREAT, I INTEND TO BAG MOBY DICK!

I'M LATE. DON'T WAIT UP FOR ME.

DON'T WORRY, I PLAN TO BE PRETTY LATE MYSELF!

SLAM!

MUCH LATER *in Silver Lake...*

...WELL, UH...I LIKE YOUR PLACE...I SEE YOU HAVE A VIEW OF THE HOLLYWOOD SIGN, SORT OF.

WHO GIVES A FUCK ABOUT THE HOLLYWOOD SIGN? I HAVE A MUCH BETTER VIEW OF SANTA MONICA BOULEVARD! ON A FRIDAY NIGHT LIKE THIS, I CAN WATCH ALL THE HOT STUDS ON THE STREET DOWN THERE, CRUISING UP THE HILL TO THE DETOUR, CRUISING DOWN THE HILL AND INTO THE *GAUNTLET...*

UH,...MAYBE I SHOULD MOVE AWAY FROM THE WINDOW; I GET VERTIGO...SURE IS HOT IN HERE!

I CAN IMAGINE! LET ME HELP YOU WITH YOUR JACKET...FOR STARTERS...

WOOOPS!

MY WALLET... IT JUST WON'T FIT IN THE SKIMPY POCKETS OF THESE DAMN LEATHER BREECHES.

YOU CERTAINLY HAVE ENOUGH PICTURES OF LEONARD IN THERE... WHAT, ONLY TWO SHOTS OF YOUR *KIDS?*...I SWEAR, YOU'VE GOT ENOUGH OF LEONARD IN THAT WALLET FOR A *WHOLE PHOTO ALBUM!*

I GUESS SO...THIS ONE, WITH LEONARD AND COIT TOWER, IS MY FAVORITE. WE WERE IN SAN FRANCISCO FOR THE WEEKEND, LAST VALENTINE'S DAY. LEONARD MADE RESERVATIONS AT ONE OF THOSE INNS IN THE CASTRO, A ROMANTIC OLD VICTORIAN ROW HOUSE...

...ISN'T IT FUNNY HOW ONE PHOTOGRAPH CAN BRING BACK A FLOOD OF MEMORIES? ...HMMM.... WE HAD TO PARK THREE BLOCKS AWAY AND WALK TO THE INN THRU A SEA OF MEN; AFTER FIVE YEARS TOGETHER, LEONARD WAS THE ONLY ONE I SAW! ...WHEN WE GOT TO OUR ROOM, I FOUND THE BOTTLE OF SPUMANTE AND THE HEART-SHAPED CHOCOLATE CAKE LEONARD HAD ORDERED. IT READ, "CAN'T HELP LOVIN' THAT MAN O' MINE"...

HILARIOUS!

...LEONARD LOVES ME...LEONARD **LOVES ME!** I LOVE LEONARD! ...AND I'M JUST **THROWING IT ALL AWAY!!** ...I SHOULDN'T BE HERE! I CAN'T DO THIS!...

...I CAN'T...

I WOULDN'T WORRY ABOUT IT, I'M SURE YOU WON'T... AT LEAST IT'S NOT TOO LATE TO GET DOWN THE HILL.

MEANWHILE DOWN THE HILL...

...BUT OF COURSE I KNEW ROCK, WE WERE FRIENDS. HE WOULDN'T DREAM OF THROWING A PARTY WITHOUT INVITING ME, HON...

...POOR OL' ROCK—HEART OF GOLD! SUCH A SHAME; THE ATTITUDES IN THIS TOWN THAT KEPT HIM IN THE CLOSET ALL THOSE YEARS, AND THEN, SUDDENLY, TRAGICALLY, THE WHOLE FUCKING WORLD KNEW... BUT, THEN, HE WASN'T ALONE IN THERE. LET ME TELL YA, HON, WHEN YA KNOW AS MANY STUDIO INSIDERS AS I DO, YA FIND OUT WHO ISN'T, WHO IS, AND WHO'S MAKIN' IT WITH WHO... THE DIRT I COULD DISH ABOUT SOME OF THE SO-CALLED MACHO LEADING MEN IN THE BUSINESS—HONEY, YOUR EARS WOULD **BURN!** ....BUT, THEN, THERE ARE **SOOO** MANY **PHONIES** IN THIS TOWN...

I KNOW, TELL ME ABOUT IT.

GEEEZ, I HAVE LOST THE TOUCH!

...BLAH, BLAH...HIGH CONCEPT...BLAH, BLAH... GROSS BOX OFFICE...BLAH, BLAH...NICE ASS... BLAH, BLAH...NIELSONS...BLAH, BLAH...DO LUNCH...BLAH, BLAH...NINE INCHES, AT LEAST! ...BLAH, BLAH...ALL PROFESSIONAL PHOTOGRAPH-ERS LIKE YOU ARE PAPARAZZI AT HEART...BLAH, BLAH, BLAH, BLAH BLAH...

♪ LARRY, HONEY, I'M **HOME!**

39

40

YES.

MY HARLEY'S PARKED RIGHT OUTSIDE THE DOOR, HERE. HOW ABOUT YOUR WHEELS?

I HAVE A RED BMW—A CAR—PARKED OVER ON HOOVER. I SUPPOSE I COULD FOLLOW YOU... BY THE WAY, YOU SHOULD KNOW SOMETHING... I HAVE A LOVER.

FORGET 'IM, HE'S A BIG JERK!

OH, YOU KNOW HIM.

YEAH... SOMETIMES I WISH I DIDN'T; A REAL GOLD-PLATED, LEATHER-CLAD HORSE'S ASS, THAT LARRY EVANS. HE'S SELFISH, HE'S STUBBORN, HE'S JUST PLAIN STUPID! ALL FOR THE SAKE OF SOME SLEAZY TRICK, HE TOOK FOR GRANTED AND HURT THE ONE PERSON WHO MEANS MORE TO HIM THAN ANYTHING IN THE WHOLE WORLD. ...WHAT A BASTARD!

THAT'S MY LOVER, ALL RIGHT; A THOUGHTLESS, SELF-CENTERED, CALLOUS SHIT HEAD... ON THE OTHER HAND, HE CAN ALSO BE THOUGHTFUL, GENEROUS AND LOVING. WHEN HE WANTS TO, MY LOVER CAN BE THE MOST WONDERFUL MAN I'VE EVER KNOWN... I LOVE THAT BASTARD VERY, VERY MUCH! THAT'S THE PROBLEM.

PROBLEM?

YEAH. BECAUSE I LOVE HIM SO MUCH...

...I'M STUCK WITH HIM.

EXIT

...THE DIRT I COULD DISH ABOUT SOME OF THE SO-CALLED MACHO LEADING MEN IN THE BUSINESS—HONEY, YOUR EARS WOULD BURN!...

JIM BARELA ©1986

43

44

HEY, WHY AREN'T YOU IN BED?

WHAT?...OH, WOW, AM I IN **TROUBLE** AGAIN?

NO. I JUST WANT TO KNOW WHY YOU'RE NOT IN BED.

COULDN'T SLEEP. I THOUGHT I COULD USE A GOOD, STIFF DRINK ABOUT NOW.

SEE THERE, ON THE SECOND SHELF, BEHIND THE MEAT TRAY? THAT'S WHERE YOUR DAD HIDES HIS CARTON OF CHOCOLATE MILK. I'LL GET THE GLASSES.

MICHAEL RICHARD EVANS...YOUR MOM CALLS YOU MICHAEL AND YOUR DAD CALLS YOU RICHARD...WHAT DO YOU PREFER?

OH, I DUNNO..."**HEY YOU**" WOULD BE OK...SOMETIMES IT FEELS LIKE A TUG-O-WAR AND I'M THE ROPE.

HAVING DIVORCED PARENTS MUST BE ROUGH.

THERE ISN'T ANYTHING WORSE!

OH, LOTS OF THINGS CAN BE WORSE...GROWING UP, MAYBE FIGURING OUT HOW TO COPE WITH HAVING A FATHER WHO'S **GAY**... AT LEAST YOU HAVE BOTH YOUR PARENTS AND THEY EACH LOVE YOU VERY MUCH. WHEN I WAS YOUR AGE, MY FATHER DIED...

...LOOK, YOUR DAD BAKED SOME CHOCOLATE CHIP COOKIES. THEY WERE FOR TOMORROW, BUT I DON'T THINK HE'LL NOTICE IF WE TAKE A COUPLE.

...I WASN'T THE OLDEST LIKE YOU, THOUGH; I WAS THE BABY OF THE FAMILY. WHEN MY FATHER DIED, IT WAS MUCH HARDER ON MY OLDER BROTHER, NORMAN. NORM HAD TO QUIT HIS SECOND YEAR OF COLLEGE TO HELP MOM WITH MY BROTHER BERNARD AND ME AND RUN THE FAMILY BUSINESS. NORM'S STILL THERE, TWENTY YEARS LATER....I DO ALL THE PHOTOGRAPHY FOR OUR ADS..."GOLDMAN'S FURNITURE, 3701 WEST PICO BOULEVARD, LOS ANGELES....FAMILY OWNED AND OPERATED IN THE SAME LOCATION SINCE 1948".

...WELL, SO THERE WE WERE; MY FATHER WAS GONE, MY MOTHER WAS HEARTBROKEN, MY ELDEST BROTHER WAS HEAD OF THE HOUSEHOLD AND I WAS TWELVE YEARS OLD AND IN THE THROES OF **PUBERTY**!....EVEN IF I COULD'VE MUSTERED ENOUGH COURAGE TO TALK TO SOMEONE ABOUT IT, DAD WAS THE ONLY PERSON I WAS EVER ABLE TO TAKE MY PROBLEMS TO...

...A FEW MONTHS LATER, BEFORE MY BAR MITZVAH, NORM INSISTED ON MY GETTING MORE INVOLVED WITH THE BOY'S CLUB AT TEMPLE BETH SHALOM AND SIGNING UP FOR **SUMMER CAMP**...TWO WHOLE WEEKS IN THE SANTA MONICA MOUNTAINS, SHARING A BUNK HOUSE AT CAMP ISADORE MOSKOWITZ WITH A **DOZEN OTHER BOYS**—WHAT IF ANYONE FOUND OUT THAT I WAS **QUEER**?!...

...BUT THEN I REMEMBERED WHAT NORMAN HAD STASHED IN HIS CLOSET. BACK THEN PLAYBOY WAS THE HOT MAGAZINE TO BUY, AND NORM HAD A WHOLE STACK OF THEM. I DIDN'T THINK HE'D MIND IF I BORROWED A COUPLE OF THE OLDER ISSUES. AT LEAST I DIDN'T THINK HE'D NOTICE...

...ANYWAY, THE MAGAZINES WORKED LIKE A CHARM. I WAS THE HIT OF BOY'S CAMP; BIG MAN ON CAMPUS! AND, MOST IMPORTANT, NO ONE EVER SUSPECTED THAT I WAS ANY DIFFERENT THAN THEY WERE...ESPECIALLY THIS ONE GUY—BUT THAT'S ANOTHER STORY...

...UNFORTUNATELY, WHEN I GOT HOME FROM CAMP, I FOUND OUT THAT NORM HAD NOTICED...

TELL THE TRUTH, LEONARD! YOU TOOK THOSE MAGAZINES, DIDN'T YOU? DIDN'T YOU?!

I JUST BORROWED 'EM! I WAS GONNA' PUT 'EM BACK, HONEST!

WELL, THAT'S A RELIEF! NICE GOIN', LEN; YA HAD US WORRIED FOR A WHILE.

YEAH, BERNIE 'N I WERE BEGINNING TO THINK YOU WERE QUEER!

...YOU SEE, RICHARD, I DID THE SAME SORT OF THINGS WHEN I WAS YOUR AGE. I REMEMBER WHAT IT WAS LIKE TO BE TWELVE AND HOW I WOULD HAVE DONE JUST ABOUT ANYTHING TO BE ACCEPTED, TO FIT IN WITH THE OTHER KIDS.

YEAH, BUT I'M NOT GAY.

I KNOW YOU'RE NOT GAY, BUT YOUR FATHER IS. AND BECAUSE YOUR DAD AND I HAVE ALWAYS BEEN HONEST ABOUT OUR RELATIONSHIP, BECAUSE WE TAUGHT YOU AND DAVID NOT TO BE ASHAMED, MOST OF YOUR FRIENDS ALSO KNOW THAT YOUR FATHER IS GAY...

...BUT NOW YOU'RE ALL OLDER. SEXUAL THINGS ARE TAKING ON A WHOLE NEW AND PERSONAL MEANING FOR YOU AND YOUR FRIENDS. SOME OF YOUR FRIENDS MAY NO LONGER THINK THAT IT'S OK TO HAVE A DAD WHO'S DIFFERENT. THOSE SAME FRIENDS MAY EVEN HAVE STARTED WONDERING ABOUT YOU, THINKING YOU MIGHT BE DIFFERENT LIKE YOUR DAD... I THINK THAT YOU'VE BEEN CARRYING THAT MAGAZINE AROUND TO PROVE TO YOUR FRIENDS THAT YOU AREN'T...

...RICHARD, I'M NOT YOUR FATHER. IT ISN'T MY PLACE TO SAY WHETHER IT'S RIGHT OR WRONG. BUT I DO WANT YOU TO KNOW THAT I UNDERSTAND; GROWING UP ISN'T EASY. WHATEVER LIFE DOLES OUT TO US, WE ALL HAVE TO MANAGE THE BEST WE CAN... HERE, WHY DON'T YOU TAKE THE REST OF THESE COOKIES TO DAVID? HE'S PROBABLY WONDERING WHERE YOU ARE.

47

Leonard & Larry by Tim Barela © 1988

HAPPY BIRTHDAY TO YOU, HAPPY ANNIVERSARY TO US; HAPPY BIRTHDAY, HAPPY ANNIVERSARY, HAPPY BIRTHDAY TO MMPH... ...MMMM!

EIGHT YEARS! TO THINK, IT'S ACTUALLY BEEN EIGHT YEARS SINCE OUR FIRST DATE.

YOU MEAN OUR FIRST **TRICK**.

WELL, THE DAY WE MET. IT'S NICE THAT IT WAS YOUR BIRTHDAY; OUR ANNIVERSARY IS SO EASY TO REMEMBER.

EASY TO REMEMBER? HOW COULD I EVER **FORGET** THAT DAY? A DAY THAT WILL LIVE IN **INFAMY**! A DAY FULL OF PROMISE, YET RIPE FOR **DISASTER**! ...IT WAS A SUNDAY AND DENNIS HAD FINALLY MOVED OUT THE DAY BEFORE...

...WE HADN'T SLEPT TOGETHER IN MONTHS, BUT I WOKE UP THAT MORNING IN THIS ROOM, IN THIS VERY SAME BED WITH THE CRUSHING AWARENESS OF HOW TOTALLY AND ABSOLUTELY **ALONE** I WAS FOR THE FIRST TIME IN YEARS...

...THAT MORNING I CLEANED THE SPARE ROOM, WHERE DENNIS HAD BEEN SLEEPING, FROM TOP TO BOTTOM. I VACUUMED THE WHOLE HOUSE, DUSTED, DID THE DISHES AND THE LAUNDRY, ANYTHING TO FORGET EVERYTHING ELSE...THAT AFTERNOON, HOWEVER, I DECIDED THAT WHAT I REALLY NEEDED WAS TO GET OUT AND GET **SLEAZY!**...

...BACK THEN, THEY STILL HAD THOSE HUMONGOUS SUNDAY AFTERNOON BEER BUSTS AT GRIFF'S. THEY STILL USED THOSE TARPS HUNG FROM A CABLE TO MAKE A TEMPORARY PATIO OUT OF THAT CORNER OF THE PARKING LOT BETWEEN TWO BUILDINGS...**THOSE** WERE THE **DAYS!** WALL-TO-WALL **MEN** IN TORN LEVIS AND BLACK LEATHER SHINING IN THE AFTERNOON SUN. EVERYBODY WAS DRINKING BEER AND CRUISING AND HAVING A **GREAT TIME**...

48

...AND THEN OUR EYES MET; HIS WERE THE CLEAREST BLUE. HE HAD BLOND HAIR, A BUSHY, RUST-COLORED MUSTACHE AND THE MOST BEAUTIFUL, CHISELED FEATURES, ALL FRAMED BY A SEXY WEEK'S GROWTH OF WHISKERS THAT MIRRORED THE SHADE OF HIS RED, FLANNEL SHIRT—I WAS IN **LUST!**

...WE GRAVITATED OVER TO A CORNER WHERE, AMONG OTHER THINGS, I LEARNED THAT HIS NAME WAS LARRY AND, COINCIDENTALLY, THAT HIS DIVORCE HAD JUST BECOME FINAL. HE WAS CELEBRATING, ENJOYING ALL THE THINGS HIS EX-WIFE WOULD'VE NEVER LET HIM HAVE: A NEW MOTORCYCLE, A LEATHER JACKET, A BEARD, AN EARRING...**ME.**.

...WHEN WE FINALLY MADE IT TO MY PLACE, AS I UNLOCKED THE FRONT DOOR, WE WERE SO BUSY KISSING AND GROPING EACH OTHER THAT WE PRACTICALLY **FELL** THRU THE DOORWAY INTO THAT FATEFUL, DARKENED **PIT**, THAT **ABYSS**, **MY ENTRY HALL** ...

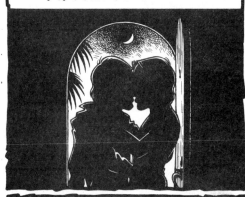

SURPRISE!!

HAPPY BIR

...**EVERYBODY** WAS THERE: NORMAN AND IRENE, BERNARD—EVEN BERNIE'S EX-WIFE, SHEILA—ALL THE **KIDS**, MY UNCLE MENDEL AND MY AUNT SOPHIE, AND, OF COURSE...**MY MOTHER.**

THAT WAS A **HELL** OF A WAY TO MEET YOUR FAMILY.

FOR AS LONG AS I LIVE, I DON'T THINK I'LL **EVER** FORGET THE WAY MY MOTHER **LOOKED** AT YOU.

NEITHER WILL I. AFTER **EIGHT YEARS**, SHE **STILL** LOOKS AT ME THAT WAY!

Leonard & Larry

by TIM BARELA © 1988

Little Victories

A **DENT!** A DENT THE SIZE OF THE **GRAND CANYON** IN THE PASSENGER SIDE DOOR OF **MY CAR!** DAMN, DAMN, **FUCKING DAMN!!**

AND YOU KNOW WHO PUT IT THERE? **A LAWYER!** A SLICK, BEVERLY HILLS, LEGAL **BITCH!** THAT'S WHAT IT SAID ON THE LICENSE PLATE FRAME OF HER JAGUAR: "SLICK, BEVERLY HILLS, LEGAL BITCH"!

SHIT, A LAWYER! GETTING MY DOOR FIXED WILL BE LIKE **PULLING TEETH!**.... AND YOU KNOW WHERE IT HAPPENED? THE PARKING LOT OF THE PACIFIC DESIGN CENTER, JUST AROUND THE CORNER AND DOWN THE STREET —I COULD'VE **WALKED** THE DAMN PROOF-SHEETS OVER TO THAT SWISHY INTERIOR DECORATOR CLIENT OF MINE!

AW, LEONARD, BIG DEAL. TAP IT OUT, A LITTLE BONDO, A LITTLE RED PAINT, IT'LL BE AS GOOD AS NEW.

BY THE WAY, YOUR MOTORCYCLE IS OUT THERE LEAVING ANOTHER **OIL SLICK** ON THE DRIVEWAY... WHY ARE YOU LYING THERE IN THE DARK?

...YOU HAVEN'T EVEN TAKEN OFF YOUR JACKET OR YOUR CHAPS YET.

NOW I KNOW THE MAGIC'S GONE OUT OF OUR RELATIONSHIP...YOU USED TO THINK THE SIGHT OF ME IN LEATHER IN BED WAS A **TURN-ON.**

CLICK

WHAT'S THE MATTER? **-SIGH-** CHUCK DIED TODAY.

OH.

CLICK

WELL, WE ALL KNEW IT WAS GOING TO HAPPEN SOONER OR LATER. AT LEAST HE ISN'T SUFFERING ANY MORE.

CHUCK WASN'T JUST MY FRIEND, HE WAS ONE OF MY BEST CUSTOMERS...SO MANY OF MY CUSTOMERS HAVE DIED...I OUGHT TO HAVE A LEATHER **FIRE SALE** AND RE-STOCK MY SHOP WITH **SWEATERS** AND **PENNY LOAFERS!**

BAD IDEA. A LOT OF **MY** FRIENDS HAVE DIED TOO, YA KNOW.

I SWEAR, SOME TIMES I FEEL JUST LIKE **MERYL STREEP.**

WHAT?

YOU REMEMBER, IN "SOPHIE'S CHOICE"...TORN BY **GUILT** BECAUSE, THOUGH MILLIONS DIED ALL AROUND HER, SHE **SURVIVED.**

OR LIKE MY MOTHER AND HER PARENTS; EXCEPT FOR TWO COUSINS, NONE OF THE REST OF THEIR FAMILY IN POLAND MADE IT OUT OF THE WAR OR THE CAMPS ALIVE. IMAGINE HOW THEY FELT! IF THEY HADN'T EMIGRATED **JUST** WHEN THEY DID...WELL, IT WAS NO MOVIE. THEY COULDN'T WALK OUT IN THE MIDDLE OF THE SECOND REEL...

...AS LONG AS THIS WORLD IS IMPERFECT, THERE'S ALWAYS GOING TO BE PEOPLE WHO DIE CRUEL, UNJUST DEATHS AND OTHERS LEFT BEHIND TO GRIEVE. BUT SOMEONE HAS TO STAY BEHIND, TO CARRY ON. MY MOM AND GRANDPARENTS WERE DEVASTATED, BUT THEY **DIDN'T** THROW UP THEIR HANDS. NEITHER CAN **WE**...LIFE IS TOO PRECIOUS A GIFT TO WASTE WALLOWING IN GUILT—THERE'S TOO MUCH LEFT TO DO. I THINK CHUCK WOULD'VE WANTED YOU TO KNOW THAT.

TIM BARELA

TO DO? **LIKE WHAT?** WE'VE GOTTEN INVOLVED, GIVEN MONEY, I PASS OUT LITERATURE IN MY SHOP. YET, AT TIMES LIKE THIS, I FEEL SO HELPLESS —**USELESS!**

WELL, LIKE STICKING TOGETHER AND CLAIMING ALL THE LITTLE VICTORIES...HELPING ONE ANOTHER, COMFORTING EACH OTHER, KEEPING UP THE **FIGHT**...YOU'VE DONE BETTER THAN YOU THINK.

I HAVE?

SURE. IN YOUR OWN **STRANGE** WAY YOU'VE BEEN DOING BATTLE IN YOUR SHOP WINDOW FOR ALL OF MELROSE AVENUE TO SEE...THAT CARD BOARD CUT-OUT OF REAGAN WITH A **REAL CONDOM** PULLED DOWN OVER **HIS EYES**—A DIRECT **HIT!**

CHUCK LIKED IT, TOO.

The Advocate 1988-1990

53

54

55

59

67

68

72

WELL, THAT'S EASIER TO SWALLOW THAN WHAT HER **HORSE'S REAR END** OF A HUSBAND SAID AT THE **TOP** OF HIS **LUNGS** IN FRONT OF EVERYBODY, INCLUDING YOUR **EX-WIFE**, WHEN HE SAW US HAVING OUR PICTURE TAKEN **TOGETHER**.

...WHAT YOU HAD TO SAY TO HIM WAS **COLD**!

I MERELY ANSWERED HIS **RIDICULOUS** ACCUSATIONS: WE WERE IN ORANGE COUNTY FOR MY TWENTY YEAR HIGH SCHOOL REUNION, NOT TO "**MOLEST** AND **RECRUIT**" TEEN AGE BOYS IN **PUBLIC RESTROOMS**! AND, IF HE **REALLY** THOUGHT SUCH A THING, **HE** WAS A **BIGGER PERVERT** THAN **I'D EVER BE**!

NOT THAT, THE OTHER.

THAT WAS JUST AS TRUE; I DON'T KNOW A SINGLE GAY PERSON WHO WAS **RECRUITED**, MUCH LESS **MOLESTED**. BUT IF I **PERSONALLY** EVER HAD A **TRAUMATIC, LIFE ALTERING, EMASCULATING** SEXUAL EXPERIENCE IT HAD TO HAVE BEEN THAT NIGHT IN '69, AFTER THE BIG GAME, WHEN **RANDY ROBERTA** GAVE ME **HEAD** UNDER THE BLEACHERS.

I ENJOYED THE TWO CENTS THAT **SHARON** PUT IN...

"YOU **RUINED HIM** FOR ME YOU **CHEAP SLUT**, I **NEVER HAD A CHANCE**!"

...YOUR **EX** CAN BE PRETTY **COOL** WHEN SHE WANTS TO.

74

Frontiers 1990-Present

81

94

95

BOSS, WHAT ARE YOU DOING SITTING OUT HERE?

OH, I JUST THOUGHT I'D STOP BY AND CHECK UP ON THINGS, MAKE SURE THAT YOU'D CLOSED AND LOCKED EVERYTHING DOWN NICE AND TIGHT. A MAN SHOULD NEVER LEAVE THE LEAST THINGS HE STILL HAS CONTROL OVER TO CHANCE WHILE EVERYTHING ELSE IN HIS LIFE IS SLIPPING FROM HIS GRASP AND TURNING TO SHIT.

UH-OH, YOU AND LEONARD HAD A BIG FIGHT AT RICHARD'S GRADUATION PARTY.

IF ONLY THE ISSUES OF LIFE COULD ALWAYS BE THAT UNCOMPLICATED. BUT NO, REAL LIFE, LIKE TIME, MARCHES ON, LEAVING YOUR FADED YOUTH IN THE DUST, DRAGGING YOU WITH IT TOWARD THE INEVITABLE— OLD AGE—A FUTURE OF SWILLING GERITOL, CLIPPING DENTU CREAM COUPONS, TRADING IN MY LEATHER JOCK STRAP FOR A BOX OF DEPENDS.... BABYSITTING MY GRANDCHILDREN...

DON'T TELL ME; DEBBIE HAD THE BABY.

JUST CALL ME "GRAMPS"! I DIDN'T STICK AROUND FOR THE BLESSED EVENT ITSELF, THOUGH. TALK ABOUT ADDING INSULT TO INJURY, THEY ACTUALLY WANTED ME TO WATCH! RICHARD ACTUALLY ASKED ME TO HELP HIM CUT THE CORD, FER CHRIS'SAKE!! I MEAN, I MAY HAVE TAKEN THE KID CAMPING, WE MAY HAVE DONE LITTLE LEAGUE TOGETHER, BUT SEVERING UMBILICAL CORDS IN TANDEM IS NOT EXACTLY MY IDEA OF FATHER AND SON QUALITY TIME.

SO, YOU JUST TOOK OFF...

...LARRY, YOU MAY BE MY EMPLOYER AND SIGN MY PAY-CHECKS, BUT, HONESTLY, SOMETIMES YOU CAN BE ONE HELL OF A HORSE'S ASS!.... WHEN I THINK OF ALL THE MEN AND WOMEN OUT THERE, DESPERATE TO HAVE FAMILIES OF THEIR OWN, DENIED THE RIGHT TO ADOPT, SOMETIMES EVEN DENIED CUSTODY OF THEIR OWN CHILDREN....AND WHY? JUST BECAUSE THEY'RE LESBIAN OR GAY.

...AND THEN THERE'S LARRY EVANS, A GAY MAN WHO WAS NEVER DENIED THE GOOD RELATIONSHIP HE HAS WITH BOTH OF HIS KIDS. TONIGHT, HIS OLDEST SON—WHO LOVES HIM—GAVE LARRY SOMETHING LOTS OF OTHER GAY MEN WOULD GLADLY TRADE THEIR RIGHT ARMS FOR...A GRANDCHILD, FREE AND CLEAR, COMPLETE WITH HIS NAME ATTACHED...BUT LARRY WASN'T THERE TO WELCOME THE NEWEST MEMBER OF HIS FAMILY. HE WAS TOO BUSY BEING A HORSE'S ASS, FRETTING ABOUT GROWING OLD AND FEELING SORRY FOR HIMSELF...

...SITTING ON THE CURB IN FRONT OF HIS SHOP, DRINK-ING FROM A BOTTLE OF CHEAP BOOZE IN A BROWN PAPER SACK!

THIS ISN'T ALCOHOL, IT'S A BOTTLE OF THAT CHOCOLATE FLAVORED SOFT DRINK WITH THE YELLOW LABEL.

YOU MEAN THE STUFF THAT LOOKS LIKE DIRTY RADIATOR FLUID?...EEECH!! KEEP IT IN THE SACK!

98

99

...WELL, I'M **SORRY!** HOW **MANY** TIMES DO I **HAVE TO** SAY IT?...**LARRY**, ISN'T SIMPLY KNOWING THAT THERE WAS A **NAOMI NEEDLEMAN** IN **MY** HIGH SCHOOL PAST GOOD ENOUGH FOR YOU? THAT EPISODE WITH HER IN THE **BACK SEAT** OF ERIC BURNBALM'S **CAR** WAS ONE OF THE MOST **TRAUMATIC**, HOMOSEXUALLY **AFFIRMING** EXPERIENCES OF MY ADOLESCENCE! MUST YOU **INSIST** ON USING THAT KNOWLEDGE TO **TAUNT** AND **HUMILIATE** ME **LIKE THIS?!**

LIKE WHAT? WHEN DID YOU SEE **ME** WRINGING **MY** HANDS, **SCHEMING** IN CHILDISH FITS OF **VINDICTIVE GLEE?** WHEN DID **I** SO MUCH AS BREATHE A WORD OF **ANY** OF THIS TO **ANYONE** WE KNOW? EVEN AT YOUR HIGH SCHOOL REUNION, AFTER FINDING OUT THAT NAOMI AND ERIC WERE **MARRIED** AND MEETING THE TWO OF THEM—**LOVELY COUPLE**—FOR MYSELF, DID **I** SAY **ANYTHING?** DID **I** TAKE **ADVANTAGE** OF THE SITUATION?

OF COURSE YOU DID! YOU WERE **DELIBERATELY NICE** TO THEM, LARRY. YOU **PURPOSEFULLY** WON THEIR CONFIDENCE AND FRIENDSHIP AND **INVITED** ERIC AND NAOMI BURNBALM TO **OUR HOUSE** FOR **DINNER** NEXT SATURDAY NIGHT!!

AND WHAT A **LOVELY** EVENING I'M SURE WE'LL ALL HAVE! A GATHERING OF OLD FRIENDS, **REMINISCING**, TRIPPING DOWN **LOVERS'**...I MEAN, **MEMORY LANE**. SUCH AN OCCASION DESERVES AN **APPROPRIATE** FEAST: **WHITE WINE** AND **QUICHE**, PERHAPS, MAYBE A ROAST **CHICKEN** WITH A NICE **SAUSAGE STUFFING**, AND, **OF COURSE**, FOR DESSERT, **FRUIT FLAMBÉ**...

UGGGHH!

...LAUREN PHYLICIA EVANS; THAT'S SUCH A PRETTY NAME! AND YOUR GRAN'PA THINKS THAT YOU'RE THE PRETTIEST GIRL HERE...DID YOU KNOW THAT YOUR MOMMY 'N' DADDY GOT MARRIED TODAY? MIND YOU, MOST FOLKS DO THIS BABY, WEDDING BUSINESS THE OTHER WAY AROUND, BUT YOU KNOW KIDS THESE DAYS. OF COURSE, NOW THEY HAVE YOU TO RAISE. MOMMIES 'N' DADDIES LIKE ME CALL THAT DIVINE JUSTICE...

...YOUR PARENTS ARE GOING TO FIND OUT THAT RAISING KIDS ISN'T A PIECE OF CAKE. IT'S LIKE BEING LEFT ALONE ON CHRISTMAS EVE TO MAKE A DOZEN BATCHES OF FUDGE, TO DO ALL THAT MEASURING AND STIRRING BY YOURSELF, JUST FOR SOMEBODY ELSE TO EAT...BUT, IN THE END, THERE'S MOMENTS LIKE THIS. THIS IS WHERE I GET TO LICK THE SPOON AND SCRAPE THE PAN AND HAVE IT ALL TO MYSELF.

YOU WOULD COME UP WITH AN ANALOGY THAT HAD TO DO WITH CHOCOLATE.

YOU HEAR SO MUCH THESE DAYS ABOUT ACTIVISTS TRYING TO GET MARRIAGE LICENCES, FIGHTING TO LEGALIZE GAY MARRIAGES...LARRY, DO YOU EVER REGRET THAT WE JUST MOVED IN TOGETHER ALL THOSE YEARS AGO, THAT WE NEVER HAD SOME KIND OF CEREMONY—YOU KNOW, A RITE OF PASSAGE?

YOU MEAN, A WEDDING? US? JUST LIKE MICHAEL DESCRIBED IN TALES OF THE CITY, NO DOUBT, COMPLETE WITH "DRAG QUEEN BRIDESMAIDS AND QUOTES FROM SONG OF THE LOON." NO THANK YOU! I ALREADY WALKED THE PLANK ONCE, WITH MY EX-WIFE.

ARE YOU SAYING THAT, GIVEN THE OPPORTUNITY, YOU WOULDN'T COMMIT PUBLICLY AND LEGALLY TO OUR RELATIONSHIP?

OH, LEONARD, OF COURSE NOT! IT'S JUST THAT I'VE DONE THIS BEFORE AND IT WAS A FARCE. BUT WHAT WE HAVE—FOR ALL ITS LACK OF CEREMONY AND LEGAL RECOGNITION—IS REAL. IF I HAD IT TO DO ALL OVER AGAIN WITH YOU, WOULD I DO IT LIKE THIS? I DON'T KNOW. WHAT I DO KNOW IS THAT, FOR OUR ANNIVERSARY LAST YEAR, WE EXCHANGED THESE RINGS, TOKENS OF THE KIND OF LOVE THAT DIDN'T NEED A PIECE OF PAPER TO MAKE IT LAST TEN YEARS...OR KEEP IT GOING TEN OR TWENTY MORE. YOU'RE MY ONE AND ONLY!

AVERT YOUR EYES, DEAR, AND JUST KEEP TELLING YOURSELF, "HE'S ONLY A RELATION BY ACCIDENT OF MARRIAGE; HE'S ONLY A RELATION BY ACCIDENT OF MARRIAGE; HE'S ONLY..."

...DON'T DO THIS TO ME, LEONARD! MOM WILL BE HERE ANY SECOND! WHERE AM I GOING TO FIND ANOTHER PHOTOGRAPHER AT THE LAST MINUTE ON A SUNDAY NIGHT?! I HAVE DEADLINES FOR OUR HOLIDAY AD! I HAVE A WHOLE HALF PAGE —PREPAID— RESERVED IN THE TIMES SUNDAY MAGAZINE!!

LEONARD, IF YOU DON'T COME OUT RIGHT NOW, THIS WHOLE MISHEGAS IS GOING TO END UP AS THE NEXT EPISODE OF THAT LOUSY NEW SIT-COM BERNIE WRITES FOR!

HEY, IT'S A LIVING.

FUNNY YOU SHOULD MENTION BERNIE, NORMAN. WHEN SHEILA GETS HERE WITH BERNIE'S KIDS, ARE YOU GOING TO HAVE HER IN THE FAMILY PORTRAIT AGAIN THIS YEAR? OF COURSE, SHEILA'S ALWAYS APPEARED IN THE FAMILY PORTRAIT...IN SPITE OF THE FACT THAT BERNIE AND SHEILA GOT DIVORCED TWELVE YEARS AGO!

WELL, LARRY AND I HAVE BEEN TOGETHER NEARLY THREE TIMES AS LONG AS BERNIE AND SHEILA WERE. DOESN'T THAT COUNT FOR SOMETHING, NORMAN?...

...THIS IS A FAMILY OWNED BUSINESS; I'M A MEMBER OF THAT FAMILY. DOESN'T THAT COUNT FOR ANYTHING, EITHER? LARRY AND I LOVE EACH OTHER. IT WOULD BE NICE IF MY FAMILY FINALLY GAVE OUR RELATIONSHIP MORE THAN JUST LIP SERVICE! LARRY IS MY OTHER HALF, MY SPOUSE, THE MAN THAT I LOVE AND I WANT THIS FAMILY AND THIS BUSINESS TO FINALLY AND OFFICIALLY RECOGNIZE THAT FACT, ONCE AND FOR ALL!!

WHAT'S GOING ON?

MY LITTLE BROTHER-IN-LAW JUST PUT HIS FOOT DOWN; APPARENTLY, LARRY AND I— BOTH— WILL BE JOINING OUR RESPECTIVE HUBBIES IN FRONT OF HIS CAMARA LATER TONIGHT.

THAT'S MY MAN!

OY GEVALT!

TIM BARELA

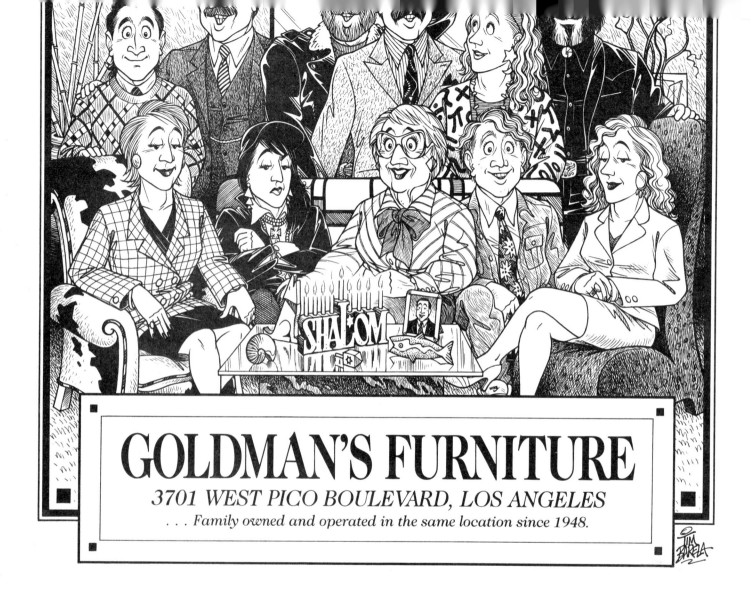

OH, REBECCA, DON'T BE RIDIC—

IT'S TRUE, MOTHER! MY TWO SO-CALLED "FRIENDS" JUST WANTED ME WITH THEM WHEN THEY WENT TO CHECK OUT UNCLE LEONARD'S BOYFRIEND'S LEATHER SHOP!

...JENNIFER AND HEATHER HAD TO INSPECT EVERY KINKY, CREEPY THING IN THAT STORE! "IS YOUR UNCLE'S LOVER CUTE?", THEY ASKED. "DO THEY BOTH REALLY SLEEP TOGETHER? DOES LARRY EVER USE ANY OF THIS S. AND M. STUFF ON YOUR UNCLE? DOES HE GIVE YOU GUYS A FAMILY DISCOUNT?"

...THEN LARRY CAME BACK FROM WHEREVER HE WAS, ALL DRESSED IN LEATHER AND THESE BIG BOOTS—LIKE SOME KIND OF NAZI! AND THEN, RIGHT IN FRONT OF JENNIFER AND HEATHER, HE ACTUALLY SAID, "HI, REBECCA" —LIKE HE KNEW ME!!

LARRY'S KNOWN YOU SINCE YOU WERE A LITTLE GIRL... ALL FAMILIES HAVE ECCENTRIC OR UNCONVENTIONAL MEMBERS; YOU GET USED TO IT AND YOU GET ON WITH YOUR LIFE. YOUR UNCLE LEONARD IS GAY, HIS LOVER OWNS A LEATHER SHOP; I HAVE A COUSIN IN WHOLESALE PHARMACEUTICAL SUNDRIES: "SOL NUSBALM, THE CONDOM KING OF BAYONNE, NEW JERSY" ...I MANAGE.

BUT MOTHER, I CAN'T GET ON WITH MY LIFE! MY LIFE, AS WE'VE KNOWN IT, IS OVER! ALL OF MY FRIENDS KNOW ABOUT MY GAY UNCLE AND HIS LOVER, NOW. BY MONDAY, MY WHOLE CLASS WILL KNOW ABOUT THE LEATHER SHOP. IT'S JUST A MATTER OF TIME BEFORE EVERYBODY GOES THERE, DROPPING MY NAME, BUYING ALL KINDS OF KINKY FASHION ACCESSORIES THAT THEY'LL WEAR TO SCHOOL WHERE I'LL NEVER BE ABLE TO SHOW MY FACE EVER AGAIN!!

REBECCA, WHO TOLD YOUR FRIENDS ABOUT YOUR UNCLE, HIS LOVER AND THE LEATHER SHOP TO BEGIN WITH?

WELL, I DID.

BUT, I NEVER WOULD HAVE IF I HAD KNOWN THAT THEY WERE ALL GONNA THINK THAT IT WAS COOL!

GO WASH UP FOR SUPPER.

TIM BARELA

IF A COUPLE OF OUR WOMEN FRIENDS HAD JOINED US LAST NIGHT, **THEY** WOULD CERTAINLY HAVE A THING OR TWO TO SAY—MAINLY ABOUT HOW **WE JUST SAT THERE**, POLITELY LISTENING TO LUCY-MAY TELLING STORIES ABOUT HER **LIFE** EXPERIENCES AS A **CHEERLEADER** AND A **PROM QUEEN**, SILENTLY WATCHING AS SHE WAITED ON DALE **HAND** AND **FOOT**, LIKE SOME **INCESSANTLY PERKY, VIRULANTLY TEXAN** VERSION OF A **STEPFORD GIRLFRIEND!**

LEONARD, MY BROTHER HAS **NEVER** OBJECTED TO **OUR** RELATIONSHIP. IF SOME EMBARRASSINGLY NAIVE, SMALL TOWN EIGHTEEN-YEAR-OLD WANTS TO PLAY **BIMBO** TO DALE'S **SEXIST PORKER**, IT'S **NONE OF OUR BUSINESS.**

BUT SHE **IS** JUST **EIGHTEEN;** DALE'S OLD ENOUGH TO BE **HER FATHER!** SHE DOESN'T KNOW THAT, BEFORE IT'S EVEN BEGUN, SHE'S THROWING HER **WHOLE LIFE** AWAY TO BE NOTHING MORE THAN YOUR BROTHER'S TIRELESS **SERVANT,** FAITHFUL **BED WARMER** AND WILLING **BOOT LICKER!**

LEONARD!...

THAT'S RIGHT, JUST ASK MY BROTHER, **LARRY**...

...BELIEVE ME, LARRY HAS LOTS OF **BOOT POLISH** AND STUFF YOU CAN USE. JUST MAKE SURE TO SHINE UP THE LITTLE SILVER PART **SEPARATELY** WITH THE SAME GOOP YOU USED ON MY **BELT BUCKLE.**

ALL RIGHTY. BUT FIRST I'M GONNA GO TA THAT BIG SUPERMARKET UP ON SANTA MONICA BOULEVARD 'N' GET A BOTTLE OF THAT SPECIAL DETERGENT SO I CAN DO YER **LAUNDRY**... I JUST **HATE** SEEIN' **RASH** ALL OVER YER **CUTE, SENSITIVE** LIL' **BUMMY.**

...MORE **COFFEE?**

WELL, IT LOOKS LIKE **SEXIST PORKER, FIRST CLASS** JUST PROMOTED WILLING BOOT LICKER TO **LOYAL ASS KISSER.**

MORNIN' Y'ALL!

SHHHH!

111

...I DIDN'T KNOW THAT NORMAN AND IRENE WERE BRINGING NATHAN WITH THEM THIS AFTERNOON. FOR HEAVEN'S SAKE, NATHAN IS MY NEPHEW! I WAS JUST BEING A GOOD HOST; I OFFERED HIM SOME MILK AND COOKIES.

THIS WAS A BRAND NEW PACKAGE OF FUDGY BEARS; IT LOOKS LIKE IT'S BEEN RAVAGED BY A PLAGUE OF LOCUSTS! THESE WERE MY COOKIES, LEONARD—MINE!!

UNBELIEVABLE! —THAT A THIRTY-NINE-YEAR-OLD MAN COULD MAKE SUCH A FUSS OVER THE LOSS OF A FEW CHOCOLATE COVERED TEDDY BEAR COOKIES TO A MERE CHILD.

"A MERE CHILD"? NATHAN IS FIFTEEN; HE PRACTICALLY HAS HIS LEARNER'S PERMIT! WHEN I WAS HIS AGE, I WAS SNEAKING CANS OF MY FATHER'S BEER. YOU SHOULD'VE OFFERED NATHAN A BUD! ...YOU JUST HAVE NO RESPECT FOR OTHER PEOPLE'S THINGS, LEONARD.

LARRY, WHAT SIGNIFICANCE CAN A FEW COOKIES HAVE IN VIEW OF THE GREATER BULK OF THIS RATHER AMPLE HOUSEHOLD CHOCOLATE LARDER OF YOURS, ANYWAY? ...CHOCOLATE KISSES, MINTS, COCOA PUFFS, —IN THE REFRIGERATOR—A WHOLE GALLON OF CHOCOLATE MILK, A JAR OF HOT FUDGE SAUCE FOR THE CHOCOLATE CHIP ICE CREAM IN THE FREEZER, A BIG BOTTLE OF...

...HEY, WHAT HAPPENED TO MY NEW JAR OF SMOKED HERRING AND SOUR CREAM? I JUST BOUGHT THIS LAST WEEK; I HADN'T EVEN OPENED IT YET; IT'S HALF GONE! ...DO YOU KNOW ANYTHING ABOUT THIS? YOU DON'T EVEN LIKE SMOKED HERRING AND SOUR CREAM.

UH, ...WELL, MEGAN LIKES IT. IN FACT, MEGAN LIKES IT A LOT... SHE CAME FOR A VISIT THE OTHER DAY AND, WELL, YOU KNOW, "I WAS JUST BEING A GOOD HOST."

MEGAN? WHO THE HELL IS MEGAN?

MEGAN IS, WELL, MEGAN—ONE OF THE NEIGHBORS. SHE LIVES NEXT DOOR, COMES BY TO VISIT ME ALL THE TIME... YOU KNOW MEGAN: BLOND HAIR, BIG, BEAUTIFUL GREEN EYES...

...LONG, FLUFFY STRIPED TAIL.

YOUR SURVIVING FUDGY BEARS NEEDN'T ANTICIPATE NATHAN'S NEXT VISIT FOR THEIR IMMINENT DEMISE. THE NEXT LARGE, SHAGGY STRAY DOG THAT WANDERS INTO THE YARD WILL DO QUITE NICELY.

117

119

125

127

129

130

131

THIS IS **MARY HART** WITH THE **E.T.** NEWSREEL... LAST NIGHT, THE TRENDY EATERY OF THE STARS, **SPAGO**, PLAYED HOST TO A PARTY HONORING **B** MOVIE KING, **ANDRE MANCESKU**, PRODUCER OF THE SMASH HIT, **"NINJA BABES"**, HOME VIDEO TRILOGY. ACCOMPANYING ANDRE WAS THE RAVEN HAIRED, TEXAS BORN MEGA-HUNK, **MERLE OBERON**, THE PRODUCER'S LATEST "DISCOVERY." ANDRE'S USUAL COMPANION, **LUCILLE MAY**, STAR OF **"NINJA BABES, THREE"**, WAS **NOWHERE** TO BE SEEN **ALL EVENING**. TODAY, ALL OF HOLLYWOOD IS **ABUZZ**...

...BECAUSE YOU COULD'VE BEEN **ARRESTED**, THAT'S WHY! I SWEAR, DALE, THE LAST TIME YOU CAME HERE TO VISIT, LEONARD CALLED YOU A "**NEANDERTHAL**". THIS TIME, YOU AND VAN DIDN'T HAVE TO PROVE HIM RIGHT BY **BREAKING INTO** SOMEONE'S HOUSE AND **PHYSICALLY ABDUCTING** YOUR OLD GIRL FRIEND, LUCY-MAY, LIKE A COUPLE OF **CAVE MEN IN HEAT**! **GEEZ**, WHAT WERE YOU THINKING! YOU'RE JUST LUCKY THAT LUCY WOULDN'T PRESS CHARGES AGAINST HER BROTHER.

YOU KNOW, LUCY **ISN'T** A CHILD OR SOME KIND OF **MOONIE** OR ANYTHING. SHE'S A REASONABLY SUCCESSFUL YOUNG ADULT WHO CAN MAKE HER OWN DECISIONS. IF SHE WANTS TO LIVE IN L.A. AND "**FLAUNT HER BOSOMS**" IN B MOVIES, THAT'S **HER BUSINESS**. DID YOU ACTUALLY THINK THAT **KIDNAPPING** AND SPIRITING HER ACROSS THE STATE LINE FOR **RE-PROGRAMING** WOULD WORK?!

IF I WERE YOU, I'D **HIGHTAIL IT** BACK TO TEXAS BEFORE TOO LONG. THAT CRAZY ROMANIAN MOVIE PRODUCER IS THE **WILD CARD** HERE. HE CAN STILL PRESS **BREAKING AND ENTERING** CHARGES. HE'S RICH, INFLUENTIAL AND PROBABLY HAS A **KENNEL** FULL OF **RABID LAWYERS** WHO CAN MAKE YOUR LIVES **MISERABLE**.

WELL, LUCY'S **ALREADY** MADE MY LIFE MISERABLE **FOR HIM**. BUT THEN, IT'S MY OWN DAMN FAULT, YEARS AGO, FER TEACHIN' LUCY HOW TA DEFEND HERSELF BY **KICKIN'** A MAN WHERE **IT MATTERS**... I HOPE YA DON'T MIND, FELLAS, IF I EAT MY SUPPER **STANDIN' UP**.

...AS FAR AS GETTIN' BACK TA TEXAS GOES, **I CAN'T WAIT**! I JUST WANNA GET BACK HOME TA TYLERVILLE WHERE LIFE 'N' FOLKS ARE **NORMAL**...THIS PLACE —**CALIFORNIA, HOLLYWOOD**— DOES THINGS TA PEOPLE, IT **SEDUCES** 'EM! FIRST IT WAS MY BABY SISTER, NOW IT'S MY **BEST FRIEND, MERLE**. HE STARTED ACTIN' STRANGE WHEN HE FOUND OUT THAT WE'D HAV'TA **SLEEP TOGETHER**, THEN HE TOLD ME THAT **HE LOVES ME**. NOW MERLE'S GONE 'N' RUN OFF TA MAKE **MOVIES** WITH THAT SAME **CRAZY PRODUCER**! WHEN HE CAME BACK FER HIS STUFF HE SAID, "WHEN I BECOME **RICH 'N' FAMOUS**, I'M COMIN' BACK FOR YA"...

...**COMIN' BACK** FER **ME**?! JUST WHAT THE **HELL** DO YA THINK HE MEANT BY **THAT**?

VAN, WE SHOULD **TALK**...

133

136

140

GEEZ, IS THIS DÉJÀ VU OR WHAT?! IT SEEMS LIKE IT WAS EXACTLY A YEAR AGO THAT THE TWO OF US WERE HERE IN THIS KITCHEN, FIXING DINNER—PASTA AND SALAD, NO LESS—AND WATCHING DAVID AND COLLIN BEING INTERVIEWED ON THE LOCAL NEWS ABOUT THE TWO OF THEM WANTING TO GO TO THEIR PROM TOGETHER. ...UH-OH, THERE THEY ARE!

OH, LOOK, HASN'T DAVID GROWN TO BE HANDSOME!

...AND HERE WE ARE AGAIN, HAVING TO DEAL WITH PHONE CALLS UP THE WAZOO AND VICIOUS T.V. NEWS BARBIE DOLL PIRANHAS SHOVING MICROPHONES IN OUR FACES. OF COURSE, THEY'RE JUST WHETTING THEIR APPETITES IN ANTICIPATION OF THE MAJOR BLOOD LETTING IN A COUPLE OF MONTHS OVER GAYS IN THE MILITARY... HUMPH. AND ALL BECAUSE A FEW JUNIOR RAMBOS WHO WERE PERFECTLY WILLING TA TRAVEL HALF WAY 'ROUND THE WORLD TA KICK SADDAM HUSSEIN'S BUTT ARE TOO SCARED SHITLESS THAT SOME LITTLE QUEER MIGHT LOOK TWICE AT THEIR PEE-PEE IN THE SHOWER!

WELL, I THINK WE SHOULD BE GLAD THAT ALL THOSE QUASI-MACHO, LITTLE GI JOES ARE SWEATING OUT THE OVERBLOWN PROSPECTS OF BECOMING THE UNWILLING OBJECTS OF SEXUAL HARASSMENT AND GETTING A DOSE OF THEIR OWN MEDICINE. AND WE HAVE OUR NEW PRESIDENT TO THANK FOR MAKING IT ALL POSSIBLE!

...WE ALSO HAVE BILL TO THANK FOR THE DEMOCRATS TAKING ORANGE COUNTY FOR THE FIRST TIME IN GOD KNOWS HOW LONG AND SWEEPING IN A WHOLE SLEW OF NEW SCHOOL BOARD MEMBERS WITH HIM—THEY SAID, "YES"! DAVID AND COLLIN ARE GOING TO THE PROM! YOU SHOULD BE HAPPY AND YOU SHOULD BE PROUD OF YOUR SON FOR STICKING BY HIS GUNS AND COMING OUT ON TOP.

OH, DON'T GET ME WRONG, I AM PROUD OF DAVID. IT'S JUST THAT CONSENTING TO BE INTERVIEWED, THIS TIME AROUND, WASN'T A PICNIC.... ANSWERING ALL THOSE QUESTIONS, TRYING TO RUN MY BUSINESS AND DEAL WITH A STORE FULL OF SURLY CAMERA CREWS ALL MORNING.... AT LEAST THAT ONE SOUND MAN WAS KIND'VE CUTE.

...ANYWAY, WE MOVED OUTSIDE AND FINISHED THE INTERVIEWS ON THE SIDEWALK... YEAH, THIS YEAR, I THOUGHT IT WAS IMPORTANT TO SHOW MY FACE, TO STAND BY MY SON AND LET PEOPLE KNOW THAT WE GAY FOLKS AREN'T A BUNCH OF SWISHY, SILLY, SHALLOW, SUPERFICIAL...

LOOK, THERE YOU ARE.

OH MY GOD, AM I REALLY THAT FAT?!

...DO I ACTUALLY HAVE THAT MUCH GRAY IN MY BEARD? UGGGH, JUST LOOK AT ALL MY CROW'S-FEET AND SUNFRECKLES! I MUST'VE BEEN OUT OF MY MIND TO GO OUT IN FRONT OF A CAMERA IN BROAD DAYLIGHT; I LOOK LIKE THE DAWN OF THE LIVING DEAD!!

MAYBE, BUT IT'S PURELY SUPERFICIAL.

WELL, AFTER THE PROM, COLLIN AND I WERE OUT PARTYING WITH OUR FRIENDS PRACTICALLY ALL NIGHT. WE ENDED UP ON THE BEACH IN BALBOA. WE JUST WANTED TO BE ALONE TOGETHER, TO GO FOR A WALK, TO WATCH THE SUN COME UP... SUDDENLY, THEY WERE JUST THERE. THEY WERE OUR AGE AND IN TUXEDOS, TOO, SO THEY MUST'VE BEEN AT ANOTHER PROM. ABOUT FOUR OR FIVE OF THEM AND ALL REALLY DRUNK.... I DON'T REMEMBER MUCH AFTER HEARING ONE OF THEM SAY SOMETHING ABOUT "THE TWO FAGGOTS WHO WERE ON T.V." OF COURSE, AFTER COLLIN WAS LAYING THERE, BLEEDING, ANOTHER ONE SCREAMED, "WATCH IT, YA MIGHT GET AIDS!" ...AND THEY TOOK OFF.

...WE'RE LUCKY, I GUESS. THERE COULD'VE BEEN ROCKS ON THE BEACH. THEY COULD'VE DONE TO COLLIN WHAT THOSE OTHER KIDS DID TO THAT GUY DOWN IN LAGUNA. THEY COULD'VE HAD A GUN. ...OH GOD, THIS IS ALL MY FAULT!

ALL THIS WAS MY IDEA... THE PROM, TAKING OUR DEMANDS TO THE SCHOOL BOARD, CALLING THAT FIRST T.V. STATION... I TALKED COLLIN INTO GOING ALONG WITH IT ALL! IF I HADN'T, MAYBE... IF WE'D ONLY KEPT QUIET...

NO, IT ISN'T! HOW ON EARTH COULD IT BE YOUR FAULT?

I LOVE COLLIN, DAD! I NEVER INTENDED TO DO ANYTHING THAT WOULD END UP HURTING HIM!

OF COURSE YOU DIDN'T! ...STANDING UP FOR WHAT YOU BELIEVE IN IS NEVER EASY. THIS CRAPPY WORLD IS FULL OF THE ASSHOLES WHO KEEP IT THAT WAY. SOMETIMES, PEOPLE WHO REFUSE TO REMAIN QUIET GET HURT AND ASK THEMSELVES IF THE EFFORT WAS WORTH ALL THE PAIN. WELL, KEEPING YOUR MOUTH SHUT CERTAINLY MAY BE EASIER, BUT LIFE IS NEVER WORTH LIVING HIDING IN THE SHADOWS!

YA KNOW, COLLIN WAS OUT COLD MOST OF THE TIME, AFTERWARDS. BUT, ON THE WAY TO THE HOSPITAL, IN THE AMBULANCE, HE CAME TO AND HE TURNED HIS HEAD TO LOOK STRAIGHT AT ME AND HE SAID, "WELL, DID WE KICK THEIR BUTTS?"

YOU'RE RIGHT. YOU'VE BEEN A TERRIBLE INFLUENCE ON THAT POOR INNOCENT, IMPRESSIONABLE BOY! YOU REALLY MUST STOP ENCOURAGING HIM LIKE THAT.

144